ELECTRICAL HISTORY

ISBN 0-945495-53-6

Tom Henry has written over twenty electrical books, taught over 18,000 electricians throughout the world.

1996 was the beginning of our new home study program "Learn to be an Electrician" in ten animated videos with modules; available throughout the world.

For information call 1-800-642-2633

Visit our Web site at:
http://www.code-electrical.com

Introduction

This book was written in appreciation of the more than 15 million men and women that work in the electrical industry to keep the lights burning every second, every minute, 24 hours a day, everyday.

Try a 100°F day without electricity and you'll soon realize the importance of the role these people play in our everyday life. The hospitals and airport traffic controllers are on emergency power, the high rise office building without air conditioning is now an incubator with no ventilation. Traffic is jammed for miles as the traffic lights are not operational.

The ability to generate large amounts of electricity has provided us with a very comfortable way of life. Television, computers, satellite communications, heating and cooling systems, etc. These electrical and electronic marvels of today all began with curiosity some 2,500 years ago.

Most of us have heard and used the words "volts", "amps", "watts", and "ohms". Now we will learn how these words came about in our study of Electrical History.

Electricity didn't turn America on overnight. It was new, different, and scary.

Modern science was not created by one sudden leap forward, but advanced via a series of steps - some big, some small; some helpful, some not.

In the beginning, it was impossible for mankind to understand something they couldn't touch.

The ancient Greeks were the first to question the nature of attraction of amber and lodestone. These two substances continued to interest the learned and amuse or frighten the ignorant.

The very smallest of nature's electrical phenomena first aroused curiosity without fear. The tiny powers of attraction of two curious substances: Amber and lodestone. Their close relationship was always sensed but undiscovered before the modern age of electricity; the nineteenth century.

In the 19th century, one great mind would further the discoveries made by another great mind, only to have this work improved upon by yet another great mind.

From the beginnings in Europe the urge was greater to define electricity in concrete terms. If men could not reduce electricity to a substance, they could at least describe it as though it were one. At this time is when the analogies occured; electric and magnetic fluids, electric current, flowing like water in a pipe.

The discoveries in electricity came from astronomers, physicians, teachers, chemists, bookbinders, mathematicians, portrait painters, engineers, physicists, printers, professors, instrument makers, and scientists from all over the world.

One was a doctor for the Queen of England, one was dismissed from school as being retarded, one was electrocuted, some were laughed at, thrown in jail, some given the Nobel prize, one's mother was illiterate, one was physically deformed, one was the greatest mathematician of all time, one had only three months of schooling and deaf. Some rich, some poor, some lucky, and some were regarded as secondary only to Isaac Newton and Albert Einstein in the world of science.

To define the word "science", one ancient philosopher wrote: "Science is the classification of human ignorance." Whereas history was defined as "the art of choosing among many lies the one which resembles the truth."

The scientist seeks something beautiful but elusive, intangible, ill-defined: He calls it *truth*. He believes that his efforts and discoveries lead him nearer to it. He does not know what it is he is looking for. His pleasure and his interest are in the search.

Electricity does not naturally exist in quantities. There is no rock, no liquid, no kind of air that gives us electricity directly.

There were no women scientists studying electricity. For centuries women were not allowed to study science.

 Marie Curie (1867-1934) a Polish born chemist, together with her husband Pierre, created the most famous husband and wife partnership in the history of science as they helped usher in the era of atomic power.

After her husband's death, Marie pioneered some of the earliest medical applications of x-rays and radium used in the treatment of cancer. The constant to radioactivity had effected her blood and she died in 1934 of leukemia.

Marie Curie was the first known woman in science.

The early accomplishments of black men and women were slowed considerably with the advent of slave trade. It was forbidden for a slave to learn to read and write.

The most significant advances for blacks immediately after slavery were in medicine.

During slavery they performed as "nurses" and "doctors" not only to the other slaves but in some cases to the master's family.

Some slaves wrote their own passes to freedom. Thomas Fuller could calculate the number of seconds in a year, in his head, faster than a man could work out the problem on paper. He was known as the "Virginia Calculator".

Since the end of World War II, the number of black scientists has steadily increased.

Some of the numerous electrical contributions from the black inventors include the electric clothes dryer, railroad signal lights, electron microscope, overhead wiring system to propel a passenger carrying vehicle, insulating paper used in transformers and regulators, refrigeration systems for trucks, etc.

Today, as times continue to change, there are many blacks adding to history in electrical engineering, research in electrochemistry, research in kinetics of electrode reactions, research on power generation and systems, research in the physics of electrons, etc.

Clarence Nathaniel Wilson born April 14, 1943 in Charleston, South Carolina. Started at age 12 to show an interest in electricity by learning television repair.

He has dedicated over 40 years to the electrical industry.

Today Mr. Wilson is the chief electrical inspector for the city of Orlando, Florida.

Did Edison invent the light bulb, Marconi the radio, Bell the telephone, Morse the telegraph? The answers are no. They didn't invent the wheel. They were instrumental in making it better and in some cases obtaining the patent.

Electrical history goes back before Christ and brings us to the computer age. Along this journey you will discover it took several people along the way to make the light bulb glow.

The world works and lives at the end of a wire. And now we will pay tribute to the many people that made it possible.

The journey won't end with this book, as we are constantly discovering new inventions that will someday even take us to the stars.

GREEK WORDS

Piezen - meaning to press, pressure

Elektron - amber

Thermo - heat

Poly - more than one

Atom - indivisible

Telephone - to speak at a distance

Kilo - thousand

Static - standing, at rest

Delta - symbol Δ, the 4th letter of the Greek alphabet

Theta - symbol θ

Omega - symbol Ω

The Beginning

First there was lightning which lit up the sky. There was the attraction of rubbed amber for tiny bits of lint, dust, and feathers. But the human need to explain and justify was not, until our own times, satisfied by scientific reasoning.

For century after century man was knowledgeable of the barely noticeable forces; electrostatic attraction in amber and the magnetic attraction in lodestone, but went no further.

The earliest useful concept of electricity, among the early Greeks, was that it was not a thing but a property, an attribute of certain substances. Many knew of these amber and lodestone powers, but few asked the question, "why?" Not until the time of the early Greeks did man ask "why?"

Approximately seven centuries before Christ, Thales of Miletus, an astronomer offered a brief explanation: He suggested that these substances had a *soul* within them, that they were alive, because they could attract objects. This was the beginning of scientific curiosity and there was no better theory offered for another 2000 years.

Amber is not a stone, gem, or mineral. It is a harden tree resin that is millions of years old. Unlike other fossils, it is organic. It even burns.

Amber is often called "an organic jewel." Gold is the most predominant color, followed by yellow and red, but amber comes in dozens of colors, including rare greens and blues ranging from transparent to opaque.

Today amber exibits display pieces that are 94 million years old and the largest piece of transparent amber ever found weighed 33 pounds.

The Greek word for amber is *elektron*. Rubbed amber would attract light objects.

The relationship between electricity and magnetism is the foundation to learning about electricity.

The story is told that in the year 500 B.C., a shepherd boy who lived in a Greek town named Magnesia often used a walking stick with an iron tip to help him climb the stony hills.

One day the tip of his walking stick actually stuck to a stone. He reached down and felt the stone. It didn't feel sticky, and nothing else was attracted to it. Only the iron tip of his stick clung to the rock. This rock is called a *lodestone*. Lodestone is an iron oxide, magnetite, grayish-black, naturally magnetized by earth itself.

The usual spelling "loadstone" suggests "the stone can lift a load."

In China about 376 B.C. Haung Ti, a Chinese general, employed the first practical application of magnetism (lodestone) in the compass. Travelers used it to find their way. Certainly Christopher Columbus made good use of it.

Earth's magnetic north and south poles are not located at the same place as the true, or geographic, north and south poles. The north pole on a compass is located in Canada about a 1000 miles from the true north pole. The magnetic south pole is about 1,500 miles from the true south pole directly south of Australia.

Birds take advantage of Earth's magnetic field in flying south for the winter. Homing pigeons have a very small magnetic crystal located between the brain and the skull which provides them a geomagnetic field for orientation.

Magnetism is all around you from the magnet holding the paper on the refrigerator, or the telephone ringing. While you're watching TV imagine a single dot racing back and forth across the front of your picture tube. This dot is directed and controlled by a magnetic field created by a deflection yoke on the back of your picture tube. Japan has a train that can float on a magnetic field at 300 miles per hour.

Magnetism is defined as an invisible force of attraction, like an *invisible glue*. Magnetism is like electricity; we cannot see it, but yet we can tell that it exists because it produces certain effects. There is no insulator for magnetism. It penetrates everything.

In the 13th century man no longer satisfied with past theories, sought objective knowledge supported by experiment to find clear observations on the properties of amber and lodestone.

In 1576 Jerome Cardan made clear in his discoveries that amber and lodestone attractions differed. This started the explosion of inquiry that in less than four centuries would carry our Western civilization to its present state of knowledge of electricity.

In 1600 an English physician, William Gilbert (1544-1603), was the first person to distinguish between electricity and magnetism. In his book he published his discovery that Earth itself is a magnet.

Gilbert found many substances that when rubbed, behaved like amber. He called them *electrics*. He is given credit for the word *electricity*.

He was different from other scientists of his time as after he developed a theory he would build his own equipment to prove his theory. Other scientists would have workmen build the equipment.

Gilbert invented the *versorium*. This probably was the first electrical instrument to be invented. It was used to help gauge the ability of objects to attract. A modern day version of the versorium is used to study atomic particles.

Gilbert spent 12 years at St. John's College, Cambridge and graduated in 1560. His greatest contribution to the science of magnetism was his book titled "De Magnete", which was published in 1600. In his honor a unit of magnetic strength is now called a *gilbert*.

A German, Otto Von Guericke (1602-1686), carried out experiments with static electricity. In 1660 he built the first machine to generate an electric charge.

In a glass globe he cast a large sulphur ball and turned it rapidly by a crank and belt. The machine was excited by a friction by applying a cloth pad. Two brushes touching the globe allowed sparks to leap across a narrow air gap between two metal balls.

He charged one ball from another, but did not infer *conduction*, the flow of electricity, because electricity was not yet recognized as something in itself.

By moistening a string, Von Guericke was able to transmit electricity several feet over the string. Wetting it made a better conductor of electricity.

The 17th century was an extraordinary period for scientific advance. The physical tools were crude and the techniques unsophisticated, but the minds that used them were brilliant.

Stephen Gray (1695-1736), an English scientist, discovered that certain objects will carry an electrical charge (conductors) while others will not (insulators). Gray discovered *conduction*, the actual flow of electricity. In his house he sent a charge through a large pine splinter, then through a linen cord to a metal ball. These high voltage charges travelled through relatively poor conductors. He later made a list of conductors and insulators, supplementing Gilbert's list from 130 years earlier. Gray's discovery that electric charges do not fill up a body but are held entirely on its outer surface was later confirmed in the *Faraday cage*. Even today, every automobile or airplane is like a Faraday cage that protects occupants from a direct lightning strike. The charge stays on the outer surface.

Gray theorized that electrification was a *fluid,* as when wetting a conductor he even got better results.

Isaac Newton (1642-1727). Newton's discoveries were not confined to mechanical science. He did his share of electrical experimenting.

This reservoir of mathematical technique was at hand when electricity reached its point of useful development well over a century later.

His Laws of Motion and his theory of gravitation are cornerstones of present-day physics.

Newton summed up his life by saying: "I do not know what I may appear to the world, but to myself I seem merely a child playing on the seashore, diverting myself in now and then finding a pebble more smooth or a shell more beautiful than others, whilst before me the great ocean Truth lay all undiscovered."

Two French scientists, Nollet and Dufay (1666-1739), discovered the difference between static and current electricity. They found that objects charged from the same glass repelled each other, but would attract those charged from an electrified resin rod. There must be *two kinds of electricity*. There were now vitreous (glass-like) and resinous electrics, splitting Gilbert's list in two. The one form of charge attracted the other; like charges repelled.

In 1745 E.G. von Kleist was looking for a way to isolate the electric fluid. He filled a jar part full of water, holding it in one hand, applied an electric machine with a brass wire and received a shock that stunned his arms and shoulders; a shock that no man had ever felt before.

These first electrical shocks caused genuine fear.

People believed then, that an electrically charged object lost its charge in open air. They thought this was due to evaporation of the *electric fluid*.

Von Kleist, however, wondered: If a collector was completely sealed and electrified, would it keep a charge longer?

Later this same experiment was performed in Leyden, Holland by Peter Van Musschenbroek (1692-1761) a famous teacher of mathematics and he got credit for the name the *leyden jar*. It was named after the University of Leyden, in Holland where Musschenbroek taught.

The leyden jar was a capacitor. The fluid was condensed, or concentrated. The glass was an insulator separating the charged water from an unlikely conductor, the moist hand of the experimenter.

William Watson, an Englishman in 1747, transmitted the electric charge instantaneously over a wire more than two miles long. Electricity's speed was beyond imagination. With this a more immediate question came to be. Is the leyden jar sparks the nature of lightning? Is there an analogy between electricity and thunder?

An American, Benjamin Franklins (1706-1790) kite experiment demonstrated that lightning is electricity. He was the first to use the terms positive and negative charge.

Franklin was one of seventeen children. He quit school at age ten to become a printer. His life is the classic story of a self-made man achieving wealth and fame through determination and intelligence.

Franklins mind absorbed knowledge, and the results of his thinking were many and varied. He invented the first circulating library. He invented the Franklin stove and bifocal lenses for spectacles.

In 1752 Ben Franklin, with three Philadelphia friends began to explore every aspect. Franklin moved into the forefront of electrical investigation.

Franklin did not believe the two-fluid theory of vitreous and resinous electricites. He proposed they were two aspects of the same force, an excess and a deficiency of the electric fluid. He named them *positive* and *negative* which are the terms used today. He felt if lightning was electricity, then a metal rod aimed skywards and connected to earth should leak away the charges and forestall the explosion. A dangerous idea, but he was right.

The first lightning rod was not installed until 1760, in Philadelphia. Franklin was not the first to suspect that lightning might be electricity, but he was the first to reduce the argument and prove it when he flew the kite in 1752.

He picked a day when a storm was about to break. At the top of the kite, he fastened a stiff wire pointing up. At the other end of the string, he tied a metallic key so it hung close to a leyden jar. It started to rain. The moistened string began to conduct electricity. It was fortunate for Franklin that there was no lightning. The storm ahead of the storm gave him enough electricity to prove, without a doubt, that electricity and lightning were the same. Sparks jumped from the key to the jar until the jar was filled with *electric fluid*.

Three years before his death he helped draft one of history's major documents; the Constitution of the United States of America.

Franklin should be considered America's first electrician.

In 1757 a professor Richmann, a Frenchman, mounted a rod on his laboratory roof and connected it to a large metal sphere inside his laboratory. It was not grounded. During a storm he was instantly electrocuted by a lightning strike. He was perhaps the first person electrocuted in the name of science.

Joseph Priestley (1733-1804) was among Franklin's strongest supporters. He was a chemist and the first historian of electrical progress.

Priestley sought inspiration from Franklin and suggested that electrical attraction obey the inverse square law. Priestley analyzed the electrical discharge pattern that became known as "Priestley rings."

James Watt (1736-1819) born in Scotland. Although he conducted no electrical experiments he must not be overlooked. He was an instrument maker by trade and set up a repair shop in Glasgow in 1757.

Of all the inventors whose genius made the Industrial Revolution possible, he was among the foremost. He once stated: "I sell here what all the world desires to have; power."

Watt was fascinated by the characteristics of heat and its relation to steam. A steam engine that failed to work was sent to his repair shop. He got the machine running but was amazed to find that the boiler could not keep the engine running for its heavy use of steam. In 1765 he created his first and most important invention: a separate container, or condenser for the engine.

He received a patent in 1769 for an engine which reduced operating costs. In 1781 he patented one that would provide rotary rather than reciprocating action. He also invented a double-action engine and a governor to keep the speed constant.

There is no doubt that his invention promoted the steam revolution. He received a patent in 1784 for the steam locomotive.

Watt thought that the steam engine would replace animal power, where the number of horses replaced seemed an obvious way to measure the charge for performance. Interestingly, Watt measured the rate of work exerted by a horse drawing rubbish up an old mine shaft and found it amounted to about 22,000 ft-lbs per minute. He added a margin of 50% arriving at 33,000 ft-lbs.

In recognition of his contributions to science, in 1889 the *watt*, a unit of power was named in his honor.

An Italian physician, Luigi Galvani (1737-1798) experiments led him to believe that electricity was in the muscles or nerves of animals.

He made his monumental observation while conducting an experiment on a dissected frog while conducting a class in anatomy at the University of Bologna in Italy. Galvani thought he had discovered an electrical source in animals when a spark passed between the frog and the machine. He continued his experiments and about eleven years later he published the results. Galvanic electricity bears his name.

Another Italian, Alessandro Volta (1745-1827), a professor of physics at the University of Padva proved Galvani's theory wrong.

Volta discovered that electricity was not in the muscles or nerves of the frog's legs but in the chemical action between two different metal; copper and iron.

In 1775 he invented the electrophorus, a device for storing an electric charge. It soon replaced the leyden jar as the most commonly used storage system of the time. Today this is the basis of a capacitor. This invention made him famous.

His voltaic pile in 1796 was the first source of direct current electricity; the first battery.

Volta produced a continuous electric current for the first time on earth. He made a stack of a zinc disk and a copper disk, with a paper disk soaked in a salt acid solution in between them. He built up a high stack alternating the zinc, paper, and copper disks. It was the greatest of all electrical discoveries. The pile was *self charging*.

The discharges could be repeated again and again. Volta believed that the contact between unlike metals, via the conducting water, produced electricity. But Michael Faraday insisted that the source was in chemical action. The zinc was eaten away and hydrogen bubbled out at the copper delivering continuous energy in the form of electricity. Volta was wrong because his theory violated the law of the conservation of energy, making "something out of nothing." It took 40 years for this to become clear.

Most important, the pile at last opened the way for the long sought after association between magnetism and electricity. Theory after theory fell because there is no relationship between a motionless charge of electricity and magnetism. The current in *motion* was the answer.

Volta and Galvani were both right, because the moisture in the frog's flesh was the acid in the experiment. Volta did not know that by using two dissimilar metals separated by a conducting liquid that the metal is less acted upon and charged to a higher potential.

Volta's reward was to have the unit of electrical potential, the *volt*, named after him.

Sir Humphry Davy (1778-1829), an English chemist known as the inventor of the miner's safety lamp. He supported Volta's contact theory that electricity from pile came from the interaction of the metals contacting, or touching, one another.

The phenomenon of electrolysis was soon discovered, and through it Sir Humphry Davy was enabled to isolate the fortieth and forty-first elements; potassium and sodium.

 In 1785 a French scientist, Charles Augustin De Coulomb (1736-1806) discovered the laws of attraction and repulsion. He was the first to measure the *amount* of electricity generated in a circuit. In his honor the unit of charge, the *coulomb*, was named.

Magnetic poles cannot be isolated, as can electric charges. A magnet cut in two, makes two magnets and four poles. Coulomb suggested a *two-fluid* theory. This came close to our present thinking.

With an inquiring mind, he studied the effects of friction and cohesion. He invented the first precision electrical instrument. It was a complicated apparatus but it could accurately measure the magnetic force in an electrical circuit. It was called the Torsion Balance.

Until the dynamo became practical, well after the middle of the century, the voltaic cell remained the only source of current electricity. The long controversy over the source of the voltaic electricity was involved with electrolysis.

An English physicist, John F. Daniell (1790-1845) was the first to use the two liquid electrolytic solutions; copper sulfate and sulfate. The electrodes were made of copper and zinc.

Gaston Plante (1834-1899), a Frenchman, invented a cell in 1860 that would store electricity. He immersed lead plates in a solution of sulfuric acid. Once the battery was charged, it would hold the charge for days.

A French engineer, Georges Leclanche (1839-1882) discovered the way to use chemical action inside the cell to produce electricity. He inserted a carbon rod with a zinc strip inside a cylinder with a weak solution of ammonium chloride. This produced electricity, but could not be recharged.

Later Leclanche developed the first *dry cell*. He was the first to make electricity portable and paved the way for many modern inventions.

Sir Benjamin Thompson (1753-1814), an American, formulated the first modern theory of heat.

Thompson's discoveries overturned the existing idea of heat as a kind of fluid contained by substances, showing it to be a form of motion instead.

He also established that mechanical energy could be converted into heat, paving the way for the development of the science of thermodynamics.

James Prescott Joule (1818-1889), an English physicist, holds the reputation of being one of history's most dedicated men of science.

His vital discovery of the mechanical equivalent of heat that today plays an important role in thermodynamics and many branches of engineering.

Because of his father's wealth, Joule was able to devote himself to his main interest; experimental science. Joule was known as almost a fanatic for his measurement of heat produced by different processes.

His idea was one that dominated all of his research: That heat and energy are basically the same and can be changed into one another. He devoted years to measuring heat changes caused by every mechanical process he could think of.

Few scientists took the slightest notice of his work as he was a known member of the scientific circles of his day. Not until respected physicist William Thomson (later his name became Lord Kelvin) showed interest in Joule's work, was his work accepted.

The mechanical equivalent of heat is 4.18 *joules*; named in his honor.

William Thomson, Lord Kelvin (1824-1907) was best known in his invention of a new temperature scale based on the concept of an absolute zero of temperature at -273°C (-460°F).

The Kelvin scale enabled scientists to make major advances in the study of heat. It provided mathematician James Clerk Maxwell with the basis for formulating the kinetic theory of gases, which used Thomson's concept of energy of the moving molecules of substances to describe their overall properties and behavior.

To the end of his life Thomson maintained fierce opposition to the idea that energy emitted by radioactivity came from within the atom. One of the greatest scientific discoveries of the 19th century, Thomson died opposing one of the most vital innovations in the history of science.

A Danish professor of physics, Hans Christian Oersted, (1777-1851) publication in 1820 revealed his findings that the relationship between electricity and magnetism was recognized.

Oersted discovered that a current of electricity creates a magnetic field. Here was the answer after years of dreaming.

His work brought about the galvanometer. Galvanometers detect an electric current from its magnetic effect. An electric current passing through a galvanometer creates a magnetic field that causes the galvanometer needle to turn at right angles to its former direction.

Oersted was introducing a new force that enjoys the company of an electrical current: Electromagnetism. Hans Christian Oersted gave to the world the important discovery that current does not flow alone in a wire but is enveloped in an invisible force field of magnetism.

Leopold Nobili (1784-1835) devised a sensitive device to measure the quantity of charge moving past a certain point per unit of time, the astatic *galvanometer*.

 A Frenchman, Andre Marie Ampere (1775-1836), a physicist and mathematician demonstrated current flowing through a coil acts exactly like a magnet.

Ampere also showed that current-carrying wires affect each other, and that wires with current flowing in the same direction attract one another.

He was the first to establish the importance of the relationship between electricity and magnetism.

It was Ampere's discoveries that eventually paved the way for the development of the motor and generator.

Ampere experimented with Oersteds theory and worked out a rule relating to the direction in which the compass needle was deflected to the direction in which the current flowed along the wire. The "swimmers rule" as Ampere called it.

Ampere was also credited with another version of the rule, called the "right-hand grip" rule. The observer's right hand is imagined gripping the wire through which the current flows, with the thumb pointing along the wire in the direction of the current. The fingers curling around the wire, indicate the direction in which the compass needle will be deflected.

Ampere, through his experiments, was convinced that electric current was somehow the actual origin of magnetism. But Ampere was ahead of his time and it was about 60 years after his death that his theory was shown to be substantially correct.

Appropriately, in view of Ampere's famous experiments, the *ampere*, the unit of current was named in his honor.

Another Frenchman, Francois Argo (1786-1853), a physicist and astronomer, on September 4, 1820 showed that a wire looped back on itself would exert a doubled push on a magnet, going and coming, more loops added, more push. Argo's loop's and Ampere's magnetic coil led directly to the electromagnet.

William Sturgeon (1783-1850) is credited with building the first electromagnet in 1821. He is also credited with having the first working electric motor.

A German, Georg Simon Ohm (1787-1854) developed Ohm's law.

Although he discovered one of the most fundamental laws of current electricity, he was virtually ignored for most of his life by scientists in his own country.

In 1827 Georg Simon Ohm discovered some laws relating to the strength of a current in a wire. Ohm found that electricity acts like *water* in a pipe. It is a simple law that states the relationship between voltage, current, and resistance in a mathematical equation.

Ohm discovered that the current in a circuit is directly proportional to the electric pressure and inversely to the resistance of the conductors.

Ohm's Law is one of the most important things that you will use throughout your electrical career. It is a mathematical tool which is of the greatest use in determining an *unknown* factor of voltage, current, or resistance in an electrical circuit in which the other two factors are known.

The law was so simple that it was not believed. Ohm was forced to resign his professorship and live in obscurity until he was recognized 14 years after his discovery. The term we use today, the unit of resistance, the *ohm* was named in his honor.

Thomas Seebeck (1770-1831), a German physicist, was the discoverer of the "Seebeck effect".

He twisted two wires made of different metals and heated a junction where the two wires met. He produced a small current. The current is the result of a flow of heat from the hot to the cold junction. This is called *thermo-electricity*. Thermo is a Greek word meaning heat.

A Frenchman, Jean Charles Peltier (1788-1842) experimented further with Seebeck's discovery. In 1834 he passed a small current through the junction of two different metals. He found a cooling effect took place if the current went in one direction. If the current was reversed, heat was generated. Today this is known as the *peltier effect*.

Heinrich E. Lenz (1804-1865), a German born scientist, is known for finding the law governing the direction of an induced current. The direction of the current induced in a conducting circuit by its motion in a magnetic field is such as to produce an effect opposing the actual motion of the circuit.

Any induced current or voltage opposes the motion it causes. If a magnet is pushed into a coil, the induced current in the coil develops a magnetic field with poles such that the field repels the field of the magnet. The same effect is felt if a magnet is abruptly removed from a coil.

Lenz's law is; the direction of the induced current in the coil can be found by the left-hand rule for electron flow. If the thumb is pointed to the left toward the north pole of a coil, the fingers coil under and then over the winding in the direction of the current flow.

Lenz took the peltier effect one step further by showing you could freeze small amounts of water using the peltier effect.

James Wimshurst (1832-1903) designed the Wimshurst machine to produce static electricity by turning a crank on the machine. The largest machine had discs that were seven feet in diameter. The charge produced was stored in leyden jars.

Sir William Siemens (1823-1883) a German born engineer, brother of Werner Siemens.

William was the originator of the Siemen electric furnace, the open-hearth method of steel refinement.

In his later years he added to his list of inventions various improvements in electric lighting and he contributed to the foundation of electric locomotion.

An Englishman, Michael Faraday (1791-1867) made one of the most significant discoveries in the history of electricity: *Electromagnetic induction.*

Faraday who loved to read, served an apprenticeship as a bookbinder. He was fascinated with electricity and would read everything he could find on the subject. Faraday made experiments, kept notes, and drew pictures.

Humphrey Davy, an English scientist, gave Faraday his start as his assistant.

It was Oersted's discovery of electromagnetism that prompted Faraday to turn from chemistry to concentrate on electricity.

On September 3, 1821 Faraday proved that a magnetic force field will make a wire move in a circle around a magnet's pole. His discovery of electromagnetic rotation was the forerunner of the electric motor.

He showed how electrical and magnetic forces could be converted into mechanical motion by placing a current-carrying wire between the poles of a horseshoe magnet. The interaction of forces caused the wire to rotate. Michael Faraday had in fact built the first primitive electric motor.

Faraday's priciple, interrupting the field of force around a magnet will produce electricity. It does not create electricity. Because a magnet has a field of force around it we can generate electricity. Without that field of force, we would not have any voltage.

Faraday had invented the electric generator, or dynamo. His discovery paved the way for changing mechanical energy into electrical energy.

When Faraday pushed a magnet back and forth through a coil, he had no idea that the world would be using his discovery to generate electricity.

His principle for generating electricity is the same principle we use today in our power plants.

With a large amount of reading material available and a very curious mind, he was able to educate himself. Michael was attracted to the scientific publications on electricity and disagreed with many of the theories.

Michael Faraday disagreed with Volta's contact theory. Faraday believed the electricity in the voltaic pile came from chemical action, not contact. After 40 years of argument, eventually it became clear Faraday was correct.

Faraday provided the basic terminology to bring these problems into focus with terms electrolyte, electrolysis, anode, cathode, and ion which are still being used today.

His pioneering work dealt with how electric currents work. Many inventions would come from his experiments, but they would come fifty to one hundred years later.

He was hailed as one of Europe's top scientists. Today more electricity is produced by Faraday's methods than by any other means.

Failures never discouraged Faraday. He would say, "the failures are just as important as the successes." He felt failures also teach.

The *farad*, the unit of capacitance is named in the honor of Michael Faraday.

He left the actual use of his theories to those scientists who came later.

Based on Faraday's experiments, other scientists began to construct hand-cranked generators.

In 1832 Hippolyte Pixii, a Frenchman, built the first apparatus that had fixed coils wound on a u-shaped iron rod. This was the forerunner to the same generators we use today. Ampere was the one who suggested an improvement to Pixii's machine; a cam-operated switching design that would reverse the alternations and produce a more usable direct current very near to that of a battery. This apparatus developed into the *commutator* as it is called today.

An American, Joseph Henry (1797-1878) in school found science fascinating and challenging and later became a teacher.

Henry's research led him to experiment with magnets. He actually discovered electromagnetic induction in America about the same time Faraday discovered it in England in 1832.

Henry was shocked when he read of Faraday's researches in a scientific journal. Henry was quick to give the Englishman full credit for the discovery of induction.

The force these men discovered is that which *induces* a current in a conductor without an electrical connection. The agent is always magetism.

Henry took an active interest in electromagnetism. After inspecting an electromagnetic creation of William Sturgeon, he began to contemplate the development of an electromagnet with new features to increase its strength. Sturgeon used bare copper wire for his windings and spaced out the turns so that they never touched each other. Henry insulated the wire so that the runs could be wound closely together around the iron bar. In doing so, Henry was able to supply more than one layer of wire on his magnet.

He realized that a key to making a really powerful magnet was the number of turns of wire on the iron core. Europe's most powerful magnet could barely lift nine pounds. Henry's could lift over 2000 pounds.

Henry's work in electromagnetism is important because he showed the possibility of an electromagnetic telegraph. Years later Edison and Morse were to refine his discovery.

Henry went even beyond Faraday and continued to research into induction. He found that a changing magnetic field around a conductor induced an opposing current to the original current in the same conductor. This is called *self-induction*. Without an understanding of self-induction, efficient motors and generators could not have been built.

Henry's fine-wire magnet led directly to the principle of the transformer, whereby the voltage of fluctuating currents may be stepped up or down, via induction from one coil to another.

Henry developed a device for controlling circuits. The device is now known as a *relay*.

Faraday also knew of self-induction, but the credit was given to Henry. Today the unit of self-induction is called a *henry*.

Stephen Gray's discovery of the transmission of electricity over conducting threads probably stimulated the idea of electronic communication.

In 1812 was the first operating telegraph via electric current. Final discoveries that led to the modern telegraph were the electromagnet of 1825 and the relay which Joseph Henry suggested to Morse.

Actually in 1774, long before electric current, a very slow telegraph was in operation at Geneve by Lesage using wires buried in glass tubes. The modern telegraph using the electromagnet was discovered in 1825. In 1831 Joseph Henry designed the first electro-magnetic telegraph, activated by a bell ringing.

Several systems came about at around 1837. Morse had the simplest and, in the end, the most perma-nent. His system consisting of dots and dashes gained fame as the principal inventor of the telegraph.

Morse had little knowledge of electricity. His first electromagnet was wound using bare wire on an iron bar. Nobody had told him the wire must be insulated. Fortunately a friend of his knew about Joseph Henry's work. In 1837 they demonstrated the first Morse machine through 1700 feet of wire. By 1856, under Morse patents, the Western Union system was started.

 Samuel Morse (1791-1872), a landscape portrait painter, while on a voyage worked out a design on paper for an electro-magnetic telegraph apparatus and a code for sending messages.

Samuel always had an interest in science, and particularly in electricity. In 1837 he abandoned portrait painting totally to concentrate on his new invention, and within a year evolved the Morse code with dots and dashes.

On May 24, 1884 Morse sent the first message: "What God Wrought". The message was sent from Washington to Baltimore to an operator who repeated the message back to Morse. By 1851 there were over 50 telegraph companies.

The telegraph system, without relays to boost the signal at intervals, that Joseph Henry invented but never patented would have remained unworkable. The telegraph provided employment for many women.

People still fearing electricity at this time and the effects that it presented by passing over their land, actually demolished a whole line, blaming it for upsetting the weather and causing a sequence of bad harvests for the farmers.

Karl Friedrich Gauss (1777-1855), a German, was probably one of the greatest mathematicians of all time. Gauss demonstrated the method of least squares, and he solved a problem of the subdivision of a circle.

His interest in astronomy led him to experiments where he devised a method of calculating the orbit and position of an asteroid in the solar system.

Gauss made many important contributions in the field of electromagnetism and the ability to create a set of units to measure the strength of the magnetic field.

A unit of magnetic induction is called a *gauss*. When we demagnetize a video or audio tape we use a *degausser.*

In 1833 Gauss and Weber constructed an iron-free magnetic observatory where they sent messages over a three-mile line built for their experiments in electrical physics.

Telegraphy, radio, and television owe much to the basic work of these two men.

Wihelm Edward Weber (1804-1891), also a German, was fascinated by the science of sound.

Webers interest focused on the determination of an absolute unit of electrical resistance. To test his formula, he set up a coil of wire on trunnions so that it could spin in the earth's magnetic field by means of a cord or pulley. At the center of the coil of wire was fixed a pivot magnetic needle. When the coil was rotated, a current was generated in the winding and this in turn acted on the compass needle making it turn against normal deflection. By calculations including factors covering dimensions, speed of rotation, and actual deflection, the absolute value of resistance of the coil was then determined.

Gauss and Weber worked together on many experiments and by 1833 had developed the electromagnetic telegraph. Weber's law of electrical force, published in 1846, was one of the first that dealt with electron theory and the speed of electric charges.

In honor of Wilhelm Weber the large unit used to measure magnetic flux is called the *weber*.

Henry Darcy (1803-1858), a French engineer, was the first to analyze *permeability* as the flow of water through a sand-filled pipe. The dictionary defines permeate as to saturate, penetrate, or perhaps a passage.

Gustav R. Kirchhoff (1824-1887) a German physicist. He made his first big contribution to physics shortly before graduating from the university by showing that electrical impulses travel at the speed of light.

A study of the visible spectrum in the light emitted from heat chemicals led Kirchhoff to invent the spectroscope in 1859.

He caused the light to pass through a narrow slit, resulting in images representing the various wavelengths of light being studied. This was the beginning of chemical analysis by spectroscopy.

James Maxwell (1831-1879), a Scottish mathematician, translated Faraday's theories into mathematical expressions. Maxwell was one of the finest mathematicians in history.

On one occasion at Cambridge University he answered all of the questions on his exam with such great speed that he spent the rest of the time translating the exam paper into Latin, just for intellectual exercise.

Many of the electrical advances today were made possible by Maxwell's computations in the 1800s. Maxwell theorized that magnetic fields, when acting together, could produce a new kind of energy called radiant energy. He wrote in 1865 "we have strong reason to believe that light itself is an electromagnetic disturbance in the form of waves."

His contribution to electricity is that he made many of Faraday's ideas clearer. He put them in a mathematical form so they could be better understood.

A *maxwell* is the electromagnetic unit of magnetic flux, named in his honor.

Today he is widely regarded as secondary only to Isaac Newton and Albert Einstein in the world of science.

Pierre Curie (1859-1906) studied the piezoelectric effect in about 1880. Rochelle salt and quartz, natural crystals with piezoelectric qualities were used.

Some crystalline materials, when subjected to mechanical pressure, will create an electric current. This is called *piezoelectricity.*

It is named from the Greek word piezein meaning to press. In the crystal pickup of a record player, mechanical vibrations produced in the stylus in the record are transmitted to the piezoelectricity a plastic stirrup.

In 1885 Curie discovered that for every substance there is a temperature at which it loses its magnetism. This temperature is now called the *Curie point.*

Electricity went through a complex development during the 50 years between the first electromagnetic motion and the big generators that launched the electric power in the 1870's.

The electric motor was in use well ahead of the generator as the battery was already there as a source of power, and second, because it could make use of the powerful electromagnet. The generator for lack of starting current could not, and had to rely on permanent magnets.

The first motors built could barely turn themselves. Later they began to exert real force, but were very inefficient. Motors were actually useless until the generator replaced the battery.

Abundant electric power was on its was at last in 1866 when the dynamo was first introduced. A dynamo is a generator that uses electromagnets for inducing the field. Several were designed in Germany, England, and America.

The first practical dynamo was built in 1860 by an Italian physicist, Antoni Pacinotti. It created little excitement.

Zenobe Gramme, a Frenchman, 10 years later came up with a similar machine. Because Gramme was backed by businessmen who knew how to promote his machine, his dynamo became a commercial success.

At Vienna in 1873 Gramme demonstrated one of his big Gramme dynamos, driven by steam. Suddenly hundreds of minds turned to the possible uses of the dynamo for doing heavy transporting of power from place to place.

Werner von Siemens (1816-1892), a German engineer, designed a dynamo in 1866 which used opposing electromagnets to produce a magnetic field around the armature, rather than around a permanent magnet.

Siemens took a major step in advancing the development of the dynamo. His dynamo had a very narrow gap between the rotating armature and the pole shoes of the stationary soft-iron electromagnet, thus increasing efficiency.

In 1839 he was granted a patent for electroplating.

Up until now electricity was following a straight path from one discovery to another. Suddenly it changed and numerous paths of discoveries leading in several directions from power generation to communications occured. The one man that traveled down several of the paths with his inventions was Thomas Edison.

The electric light, the third great primary electrical discovery, began with Davy in 1809. During the next 70 years most electric lights were experimental.

The carbon rods had a simple arc but they burned away too quickly. In 1845 an Englishman King and an American Starr, working together produced, the first lamp using a carbon rod in an evacuated glass globe which worked fairly well.

It wasn't until Hermann Sprengel (1834-1906) invented a vacuum pump that was able to remove almost all of the air from the glass globe of the incandescent lamp that the lamp became practical.

Sir Joseph Swan of England and Thomas Edison in America added the final commercial touches.

Thomas Alva Edison (1847-1931) was one of the most well known inventors of all time with 1093 patents. Self-educated, Edison was interested in chemistry and electronics.

During the whole of his life Edison received only three months of formal schooling, and was dismissed from school as being retarded, though in fact a childhood attack of scarlet fever had left him partially deaf.

Edison had almost 150 patents on making the battery a better one.

He is best known for his work on the transmission of light and power, and improving the telegraph and telephone.

One of Edison's most original inventions was the phonograph. The incandescent light was not Edison's exclusive idea, but he found a way to make it more practical.

Edison's lights used a platinum element, burning in strings at only 10 volts. Edison realized a much higher voltage would be required to reduce power losses from the source generator. He designed a small, high resistance carbon lamp to operate at 110 volts.

He developed a better pump to obtain a better vacuum in the bulb so it would burn brighter and last longer. It took Edison and his 3000 workers nearly a year to perfect the incandescent lamp.

October 19,1879 his first successful lamp burned for 40 hours.

Edison's light demonstration in New Jersey in 1879 had special trains bringing crowds to see it.

The lamp was just a beginning as Edison had a much larger plan for a complete commercial lighting system with a central power plant. Edison designed the system in every detail from the switches in the house to the meter.

The first central commercial incandescent electric generating plant went into operation September 4, 1882 at 257 Pearl Street in New York City serving one square mile serving 52 customers with direct current.

Edison was no theorist; he would search through an entire haystack to find the needle.

He had no interest in scientific principles. He just wanted his inventions to make money.

During his career, Edison made and lost fortunes on an extraordinary scale. In some areas he had been accused of developing the ideas of others, merely adding the finishing touch and gaining the patent.

After 1870, electricity's forward steps were so gigantic, in so many directions, that it became a major force in shaping our changing world.

Thomas Edison's DC supply was restricted to short distances with a powerhouse necessary for each square mile. Supplying an area with many lights required huge copper conductors to handle the higher current.

When electricity was sent a few yards it was okay, but when it was sent over several miles its power fell off at a rapid rate. Most engineers at the time felt that electric power could never be used other than local.

The solution was found in the long neglected AC current. This alternating current has a distinct advantage: The useful voltage developed could be raised or lowered by a transformer, while direct current could not.

This enabled a powerhouse to transform the electricity to a high voltage and low current for distribution along a power line. Then, through another transformer, the voltage was lowered to a desired level at the destination. This meant that the low currents could use much smaller wires to send electricity over long distances.

Nikola Tesla was born of Serbian parents July 10, 1856 and died a broke and lonely man in New York City January 7, 1943. He envisioned a world without poles and power lines. Refered to as the greatest inventive genius of all time.

His father was a clergyman. His mother, though she never learned to read and write was known as an inventor of domestic labor saving devices, and it is to her that Tesla attributed much of his inventive genius.

Since Tesla could speak eight languages equally well it enabled him to give lectures throughout the world on his electrical inventions.

Tesla had a lot of peculiar habits. Real eccentric, he was. He had a lifelong distaste for corporate involvement and resented any form of control.

His ears were so sensitive he could hear a clock ticking two or three rooms away. He claimed that he had visions, that each time he had one of these visions, the whole thing just popped up in his mind like it was on a screen. This mental picture was complete right down to the smallest detail. He could sort of see things before they happened. He was 1000 years ahead of time.

He never acquired the habit of writing notes, always claiming (and proving) that he was able to retain complete detailed data on all of his research and experiments in his mind.

47

This was an advantage that eventually worked against him as well. Since he did not keep a notebook many of his achievements are lost. Even many of his inventions that he demonstrated to scientific societies throughout the world cannot be duplicated. Some of his inventions are lost forever. Other inventors may someday rediscover his ideas, although the trouble is that because so many ideas came to his mind, it is impossible to separate his concrete possibilities from his dreams.

For reasons which I am unable to explain, Nikola Tesla was the genius America forgot, the man who laid much of the foundation of electrified civilization is scarcely remembered. Mainly because his remarkable work was hard to understand because his records were disorderly, and because several countries, the United States among them, have apparently scaled some of his papers for possible use in weapons research. Never married, so he left no family and due to his photographic mind very few notes were left behind.

In his early school days, he solved complex problems in his head, without pencil and paper. His teachers suspected him of cheating, but young Tesla had actually memorized whole logarithmic tables!

In 1877 while he was a student at the polytechnical college of Graz, Austria Tesla's attention was first drawn to problems of the induction motor. His observation that a Gramme dynamo that was being run as a motor in a classroom demonstration sparked badly between its commutator and brushes led him to suggest that a motor without a commutator might be devised, an idea that his professor ridiculed.

Tesla continued in his mind to develop the idea. In 1881 at the age of 25, while walking in a park with a friend the idea came like a flash of lightning and Tesla took a stick and drew in the sand a diagram of the polyphase induction motor. These same diagrams were illustrated in his fundamental patents in May 1888.

Impressed by the wealth of available water power going to waste around the world, he visualized the harnessing of that great supply with hydroelectric plants capable of distributing power to where it was needed. He startled fellow students in Budapest by announcing: "Some day I will harness Niagara Falls."

In 1882, through family friends, he was recommended for a job in Paris as an engineer for Edison's telephone subsidiary, the Continental Edison Company. It was here that he was urged to go to America.

In 1884 at the young age of 28 Nikola Tesla stepped off a ship in New York City, his head full of ideas, a working knowledge of a dozen languages, four cents in his pocket, and an introduction to Thomas Edison.

Edison although totally commited to direct current gave Tesla a job at the Edison Machine Works. By 1885 he had left Edison and worked on his own until he teamed up with George Westinghouse who bought the rights of his AC dynamos, transformers, and motors.

Tesla's system triumphed to make possible the first large-scale harnessing of Niagara Falls with the first hydroelectric plant in the United States in 1886.

Thomas Edison's direct current system proved to be inefficient and was dropped in favor of Tesla's polyphase system.

In 1889 Tesla became an American citizen. He continued to work in his New York laboratories and was very successful in the invention of the Tesla coil, an air-core transformer, and in further research on high-frequency currents.

Tesla established the frontier of high frequency engineering. His lectures revealed principles of high frequency lighting, wireless telegraphy, the open-ended secondary circuit, medical electricity (diathermy), high frequency heating and welding, wireless controls, etc.

In 1890 he discovered that by aiming a low-power Tesla coil at the human body, the invisible rays could speed up the healing of torn muscles or sprains. It was later patented by another person. It is called diathermy or radiothermy.

Nikola Tesla and
his lightning coils.

In 1891 he lectured on his high-frequency devices to the American Institute of Electrical Engineers, and this lecture, coupled with a spectacular demonstration of these apparatuses, made him famous.

He proposed wireless communication by actual conduction of electricity through natural media, and working in Colorado Springs, Colorado in 1899-1900, proved the earth to be a conductor. Tesla produced artificial lightning in flashes of 20 million volts that were up to 135 feet in length. The lightning discharging could be heard for 15 miles. A feat that has never been equalled.

In 1892 after the death of his mother he became increasingly withdrawn and eccentric.

The Chicago Worlds Fair (Columbian Exposition) in 1893 gave the contract to Westinghouse to use Tesla's AC system which lit thousands of lights. The motors drove the first ferris wheel. Nikola performed demonstrations where his body would receive over 200,000 volts, vibrating a million times per second. This was the beginning for medical diathery whichs includes x-ray, microwave, and radio waves to destroy cancer cells. He demonstrated the first synchronized electric clock, electric stove, electric fans, and even an automatic dishwasher. Yes, in 1893 Nikola Tesla was referred to as "the distinguished electrician". Often called the "magician of electricity" with his scientific demonstrations he performed throughout the world.

In 1898 at Madison Square Garden in New York City, Tesla demonstrated modern guided weapons and vehicles, automated industry, robotics, and the first remote controlled boat, ideas which would not be ready for many years to come.

With the financial backing of J.P. Morgan, he began work on a worldwide communications system, and a 180 foot transmission tower was constructed at Wardenclyffe, Long Island. By 1905 however, for reasons that have never come to light, Morgan had withdrawn his financial support and the project came to an end. The tower was destroyed by dynamite under mysterious circumstances in 1914. It was said it was destroyed for security reasons to keep the enemy agents from using it during World War I.

Guglielmo Marconi was credited with the invention of wireless telegraphy until June 21, 1943 when the Supreme Court Decision ruled that Nikola Tesla had prior patents.

By 1917, Tesla was not only broke but was increasingly ignored by scientists and engineers who were engaged in developing his earlier ideas.

While his mind was as productive as ever, he became increasingly eccentric and secluded.

Tesla loved the pigeons and would walk to the park daily to feed them. Pigeons appealed to the lonely, usually poor, and eccentric persons. Important people did not hang out in city parks feeding dirty birds, but Nikola Tesla did.

He was totally secluded in his last years, living in a series of New York hotel rooms with only his pigeons as company.

In his final years, Tesla isolated himself almost completely, although he still occasionally received distinguished visitors at his hotel room. As poor as he was he still sent money to his friends that were worse off than him. In January 1943 just before his death, he sent a messenger from his hotel room with a gift of $100 to be delivered to his close friend Mark Twain, forgetting he had died 33 years earlier.

In his dying years at age 87 he would leave his hotel room window open to feed his pigeons when he could no longer walk to the park to feed them.

When a maid opened his hotel room on January 8, 1943 she found Nikola in his bed having died during his sleep. His cremated remains, most of his papers, and some of his apparatus were eventually moved to Yugoslavia, where now they are in the Tesla Museum in Belgrade.

His funeral was held in the Cathedral of St. John the Devine, in New York. Hundreds of scientists attended the services and famous people such as Eleanor Roosevelt sent telegrams.

He had planned to live to be 150, and upon reaching the age of 100, would write his memoirs, which would include a detailed record of all the data he had compiled. At his death during World War II, the contents of his safe were impounded by military authories, and nothing has been heard since as to what records, if any, were there.

In Tesla's death the common man loses one of his best friends.

In 1976 a statue was errected at the site of the world's first hydroelectric plant. The Adams plant was located on Goat Island on the American side of Niagara Falls.

The evolution of electric power from the discovery of Faraday in 1831 to the initial great installation of the Tesla polyphase system in 1896 is undoubtedly the most tremendous event in all engineering history.

Every electric motor today to run the appliances are running on AC current using the rotating magnetic field originated by Nikola Tesla.

Even though at one point he dug ditches to make a living on a Western Union project, he became a millionaire at age 32 through his inventions, but died nearly penniless.

Some say Tesla got to play the last joke on everyone at his funeral. There were reporters and photographers from every big newspaper and magazine from all over the world. Well, they were all using a quality film in their cameras, and they took a lot of pictures of Nikola in his open casket. Just after they took the last picture, a ray of sunlight hit Tesla's head from one of the stained glass windows and people heard a loud clap of thunder, but it wasn't raining. The weird thing was, all those pictures they took, every single negative was blurred. The film company couldn't figure it out. So Nikola Tesla had the last word.

October 1893 George Westinghouse (1846-1914)was awarded the contract to build the first generators at Niagara Falls.

Westinghouse invented the air brake system to stop trains; the first of more than one hundred patents he would receive in this area alone. He soon founded the Westinghouse Air Brake Company in 1869.

The knowledge he gained from his work with compressed air guided him in his work with electricity. He invented a reduction valve that permitted high-pressure gas to be delivered at lower pressure at the point of use. He reasoned that a similar device could work on electricity and found it in a "secondary generator" developed in England.

He used his money to buy up patents in the electrical field. One of the inventions he bought was the *transformer* from William Stanley.

George Westinghouse began the bitter rivalry between AC and DC that continued for years to come.

THE BATTLE OF CURRENTS AC vs DC

Telsa was AC and Edison was DC and they disagreed on which was best.

Edison fought alternating current tooth and nail. He would hold demonstrations for newspaper reporters to witness the frightened dogs and cats that schoolboys had snatched off the streets being shoved onto a sheet of metal and then electrocuted with 1000 volts from an AC generator to show the hazards of alternating current.

Tesla worked for Edison trying to improve Edison's DC dynamos. He was sure he could increase the ouput, lower the cost, and decrease the maintenance. Edison told him if he could do that it would be worth $50,000 to him.

The money would be a dream come true for Tesla as he wanted to build his own laboratory. He worked eighteen hours a day every day including Sundays until he designed twenty-four types of dynamos, eliminating the long-core field magnets then in use and substituting the more efficient short cores. Months later when the task was completed, and some of the new machines built and tested and found measuring up to his promises which delighted Edison. Tesla asked to be paid the $50,000. Edison replied, "Tesla, you don't understand our American humor." He resigned his job with Edison immediately. Some say he "tipped his hat to Edison as he left the laboratory." Tesla was a gentleman under all circumstances. This was in the spring of 1885.

After this falling out they became bitter enemies. With financial backing from A.K. Brown an executive with Western Union and others, Tesla set up his own laboratories to develop his AC ideas. Tesla was granted seven patents in the first six months and twenty-two more in the next year.

One day in 1888 George Westinghouse walked into Tesla's lab and introduced himself. Tesla was then 32 years old, Westinghouse 42. Both were capable inventors, accomplished engineers, and electrical enthusiasts.

Westinghouse listened to Tesla explain his theories, watched his demonstrations, and quickly made up his mind.

Tesla had hit upon the principle of the rotating magnetic field produced by two or more alternating currents out of step with each other. By creating, in effect, a magnetic whirlwind produced by the out-of-step currents, he had eliminated both the need for a commutator (the device used for reversing the direction of an electric current) and for brushes providing passage for the current.

Other scientists had been trying to invent AC motors but had used only a single circuit, just as in direct current, which either would not work or worked badly, churning up a great deal of useless vibration. There had not been a truly successful AC motor until Tesla invented his polyphase motor.

"I will give you one million dollars cash for your AC patents, plus royalties" offered Westinghouse. "Make that royalty one dollar per horsepower and it's a deal," replied Tesla. The two men shook hands and it was a done deal.

Tesla had arrived. But he was not a man to forget those who had placed faith in his ideas, and promptly gave over $500,000 dollars to A.K. Brown who had financed his lab. Although Westinghouse backers later forced him to get a release from Tesla on the dollar-per-horsepower part of the agreement, Tesla admired Westinghouse to the point he relinquished the royalties that would have supported him and his research efforts the rest of his life.

The phenomenal success of the Westinghouse AC systems across the nation made it clear to General Electric engineers that they would have to pay a handsome fee to get a license from Westinghouse if they were to compete in the electrical industry. This made Tesla smile, as he never forgot Edison's statement that there was no future in alternating current and that his experimenting with it would be a waste of time.

In 1890, the International Niagara Commission began its search to find the best way of using the power of Niagara Falls to generate electricity. The scientist Lord Kelvin was appointed chairman of the Commission, and immediately announced that a DC system would obviously be the best. It was not easy to challenge that world famous authority, but Kelvin eventually came to realize that if power were to be transmitted even the 22 miles to Buffalo, AC would be necessary. Thus, it was decided to use Tesla's system and generate AC with massive water turbines.

In 1892 the Columbian Exposition directors in Chicago sought electrical bids to light the fairgrounds. General Electric had recently taken over the Edison interests and held the patent on the only really practical glass bulb for incandescent lamps. Westinghouse was determined to light the fairgrounds with his new AC system. He won the contract by underbidding General Electric and built twelve 25 ton polyphase generators that lit up the fairgrounds as well as the Westinghouse exhibit.

Between Westinghouse and Tesla's demonstrations at this Worlds Fair, alternating current was the winner.

In 1893 Westinghouse won the contract for the ten 5,000 horsepower hydroelectric generators, 25Hz, two-phase. The voltage was stepped up to 22,000 volts for transmission. This overshadowed the 900 horsepower at the Edison Plant on Pearl Street.

On November 16, 1896 the Niagara Falls Power Company closed switches and began supplying electricity to Buffalo, New York 22 miles away.

Mr. and Mrs. Westinghouse pictured at Niagara Falls.

Tesla, while working for Westinghouse, set a standard of 60 hertz. At that time there was no standard for the frequency of the transmission of current. Some engineers favored 133 cycles per second. Today electric clocks which keep time are based on 60 hertz. Current changes twice 60 times a second, and since there are 60 seconds in a minute, we have an easy way to keep time electrically.

Tesla was the first to perfect the polyphase AC system. Instead of using six wires for the three coils, three of the wires were eliminated with some ingenious arithmetic and the currents in them add up to zero. These three wires are found today on hundreds of power poles. Tesla's system was the key to the heavy use of industrial AC power.

Tesla left Westinghouse to pursue his own experiments in the field of high-voltage, high-frequency electricity.

Edison had lost the battle. Even his company, the Edison Electric Company, converted to AC. Today this company is known as General Electric.

Charles Steinmetz (1865-1923), an immigrant from Germany, went to work as a consulting engineer for General Electric, Edison's old firm. Steinmetz, although physically deformed, had the mind of a genius.

Steinmetz spent nine years working on theories and calculations of AC current. He improved AC motors and generators with his patents.

At the age of 27, he formulated the law of hysteresis, which made it possible to increase the efficiency of electrical apparatus.

Elihu Thomson developed the first electric welding transformer in 1886.

Thomson held over 700 patents, the third largest held by any man. He demonstrated his first dynamo in 1878. He also held a patent for the electric meter.

A water turbine is a rotary machine that converts some of the energy of a flowing stream of fluid into mechanical energy that can be used to perform work. The first water turbine was invented in 1775 by a Frenchman, Pierre-Simon Girard.

Sir Charles Algernon Parsons (1854-1931) contribution to technology was the invention of the steam turbine.

Knowing the limitations of the steam engine, Parsons devised a steam turbine, which had a rotor in which vanes were attached. Steam striking the vanes would cause the shaft to revolve. This design increased the speed of operation from 1,500 to 18,000 rpm.

With the steam turbine's ability to generate vast amounts of power, it was the most efficient machine to utilize the heat energy of steam.

A generator must be driven by some type of machine that produces mechanical energy. Steam is the prime mover for many of todays generators. The steam turns turbines which turn the generator.

Electric power plants use coal, oil, or water for many of their large generators. Coal is burned and used to heat water into steam. The steam turns large blades of a turbine. The turbine is connected to the shaft of an electromagnet field and causes it to turn inside the stationary armature. The spinning of the magnet field produces electrical energy.

The first electric code contained 54 pages in 1896.

Rules and requirements of the National Board of Fire Underwriters for the installation of wiring and apparatus for electric light and power as recommended by the Underwriter's and National Electric Association.

The National Code is said to be the wiremen's Bible; it says "thou shalt not use this, and thou shalt not do that," and it also contains, for he who will study it, the principles which enable him to decide what he ought to do.

The code is not intended to be a cast-iron set of regulations or a complete specification of how to do construction, but it is designed to serve as the common law of electrical construction, to indicate what things must always be done, what must never be done, and set forth the principles which should be observed in order to secure safety. It is the spirit of the code, even more than the letter, that should be studied by the architect and the engineer.

It is impossible to conceive a set of regulations which would describe all necessary requirements of good work, but an observance of the principles underlying these rules will enable us to determine what material and construction is suitable and what is best for each particular case.

If a tree fell in a remote wooded area and there is no one there to hear it, is any sound produced?

One answer to this question is no, because sound is something we hear and if it is not heard then there is no sound! But the answer can also be yes, if we define sound simply as vibrations made by an object; a tree falling.

All sounds from a whisper to the roar of a jet engine have one thing in common. They are vibrations which, when they travel through the air and reach our ears, we hear as sound. You can even feel sound vibrations.

Alexander Graham Bell (1847-1922), born in Scotland, was raised in a family that was interested and involved in the science of sound. Bell's father and grandfather both taught speech to the deaf.

In his youth Bell knew as much about speech, acoustics, and the peculiar characteristics of the human eardrum as anyone in the world. And it was from this knowledge that he eventually achieved the telephone. It was said "if Bell had known more about electricity he would never have patented the telephone."

In 1876 a human voice was transmitted over a wire for the first time. Bell designed the device to work when a person speaks into a telephone, an electric current is generated by the vibrations. These electronic vibrations are then carried over a wire to a receiver. The sound waves themselves do not travel through the wire. The sound waves disturb the steady flow of the regular electrical current.

The basic patent on the telephone was granted to Bell on March 7, 1876. It was the most valuable patent ever issued. Bell was 29 years old.

Who would of thought in 1876 that in 100 years over 100 million telephones would be in use in the world.

A unit of sound level is called a *bel* in his honor. Sound levels are measured in tenths of a bel, or decibels. The abbreviation for decibel is dB.

Elisha Gray filed a patent for a telephone on February 14, 1876 two hours after Alexander Graham Bell had also submitted a patent for a telephone on the very same day. Neither man knew of the other one's patent.

In 1877 the English physicist Lord Rayleigh published a study of the resonance, vibration, and diffraction of sound. Also in 1877, the Czech-born physicist Ernst Mach studied the speed of sound, which is around 740 mph at 32°F at sea level. The speed of sound also depends upon the medium in which the sound is transmitted.

Hermann von Helmholtz, a German, developed measurements and evolved laws about the behavior of electricity and magnetism. His development of the mathematics dealing with resonance in an electrical circuit was years ahead of its time.

Von Helmholtz, in his work with the science of acoustics, showed that the quality of the voice over the telephone was not due to a single tone. To sound natural, the voice had to be transmitted as a combination of tones. These combinations are called *harmonics*.

Heinrich Hertz (1857-1894), a German physicist, laid the ground work for the vacuum tube.

He was one of the first people to demonstrate the existence of electric waves. Hertz was convinced that there were electromagnetic waves in space.

He laid the foundation for the future development of radio, telephone, telegraph, and even television.

Hertz theorized that an electromagnetic wave existed as current flowed, or oscillated, between two plates.

His amazing discovery proved that energy could be transmitted through space in the form of electromagnetic waves. He could only theorize about the similarities between these waves and light waves, but he concluded there must be some relationship. It had to be the difference in the frequencies.

In 1886 he demonstrated that it was practicable to create and detect the waves of electrical radiation. His electric-wave generator consisted of an induction coil feeding a spark gap from which a pair of plate-like conductors extended. The conductors corresponded to what became the antenna and ground wires of later radio transmitters. Hertz's receiver was a wire ring with a small opening in its circumference. When electromagnetic waves arrived, small sparks passed across the opening.

Hertz was not only able to prove that he could receive emissions from his spark transmitter, but was also able to measure their strength and determine their direction.

In 1887, he proved the existence of these waves. After his discovery, an Italian, Guglielmo Marconi became interested in these waves for communication.

He did not live to share in the excitement of his discoveries as he died at age 36 from a chronic blood disease.

While cycles per second soon became a preferred measurement, the term "*hertz*" was adopted until 1960.

Willem Einthoven developed the first EKG machine in 1900.

A recording of the heart is an electrocardiogram, or EKG. Tiny "ripples" of electric current pass from working organs through the body's tissues to the skin.

Guglielmo Marconi (1874-1937), an Italian inventor, using similar equipment developed by Hertz, was able to send wireless messages about one mile.

He was only 20 years old when he began his experiments to transmit a spark from one point to another without any wires.

In 1895 he was able to transmit from shore to a ship at sea. By 1896 he took out his first patent for wireless telegraphy, based on Hertz's discoveries but using much longer wave lengths.

In 1901 he sent the first transatlantic signals from England to Newfoundland some; 2,000 miles.

In 1909 he shared the Nobel prize in physics.

Marconi's invention had one serious drawback, communications could only be carried by means of dots and dashes. A voice could not be heard because the spark gap transmitter was not adequate for the complex waveforms of the human voice.

William Crookes (1832-1919), a British scientist, was one of the discoverers of the *cathode ray.*

In 1887 Crooke's experimented by putting a small metal cross in the path of the rays coming from the cathode. The cross cast a shadow on the glass screen beyond.

This demonstrated that rays came from a cathode, and that they traveled in straight lines, just as a flashlight shining light rays onto the cross shape would cast a shadow behind it. This became the basis for television.

Sir J.J. Thomson (1856-1940), an English physicist, revolutionized our understanding of both electricity and atoms by explaining the nature of the electron.

Thomson discovered that all atoms contain particles of electricity regardless of the kind of atom. These identical particles he called corpuscles. By measuring the ratio of their electrical charge and mass, he showed that these electrons were much smaller than individual atoms.

Thomson knew that cathode rays could be bent or deflected by a magnetic field. He devised an experiment to measure the ratio of charge carried by particles, which he believed made up cathode rays, to their mass. This involved balancing two separate forces on the particles. One produced by the magnetic field of the current flowing in a pair of coils, and the other by the electric field between two metal plates.

He remained, until his death in 1949, one of the great intellectual celebrities of British science.

John A. Fleming (1849-1945), who once worked with Marconi, developed a device in 1887 that he further refined resulting in his invention of a diode in 1904 that became known as the Fleming valve. The diode or rectifier would covert AC into nearly DC for a more useful purpose and was placed in a receiving circuit of a radio.

R.A. Fessenden developed the idea of a high-frequency alternator operating at 50,000 hertz. This wave was at a steady voltage. A voice could ride that wave with a frequency of about 2,000 hertz.

E.H. Armstrong, an American inventor, gave radio a big boost by inventing the heterodyne and superheterodyne circuits. By feeding part of the output of a tube back to its input, this means from the grid of the tube to its plate, the circuit would oscillate. This is another way of saying it would produce a steady tone. A high-frequency current would result and be used as the carrier wave.

He was the inventor of FM (frequency modulation) radio. His invention of FM lives on today as it produces a higher quality signal than does AM. FM is not affected by natural static, man-made static, or lightning.

Like light, X-rays, and all forms of electromagnetic radiation, radio waves travel at 300 million metres per second.

Lee DeForest (1871-1961), an American, often thought of as the "Father of Radio" invented a vacuum tube in 1907 that could not only detect the signals but could amplify them to a level where they could be heard through a loud speaker. Fleming and DeForest's tubes made radios possible and led the way to television, radar, and computers.

The process of light causing certain metals to emit electrons, called the *photoelectric effect,* was discovered by a German physicist, Philipp Lenard.

The knowledge of the photoelectric effect led to the invention of the photoelectric cell in 1883 by an American inventor, Charles Fritts. It provided a means for controlling an electric current by the intensity of light striking the cell.

In 1902 Pieter Zeeman and Hendrik A. Lorentz, both of the Netherlands, shared the Nobel prize for their work and other research on the influence of magnetism on radiation. The Zeeman effect refers to the widening and splitting of spectral lines by a magnetic field; a phenomenon that tends to confirm the electromagnetic theory of light.

The discovery of the photoelectric effect led many scientists to attempt to transmit pictures by wire.

Television evolved from sound broadcasting; the TV camera converts light into electrical impulses. The foundations on which television rests are the radio, the cathode tube, and the photoelectric effect discovered by Heinrich Hertz in 1887.

In the mid 1800s television had its beginnings as scientists attempted to send light images over a wire, but it was not until the late 1940s and early 1950s that television came into its own.

John L. Baird (1888-1946), in 1920, built television transmission equipment using bits of scrap metal and electrical components which used a rotating scanning disc in a system designed to transmit silhouettes. Baird's 1926 version produced a 30 line image which was renewed 10 times each second.

The disc had been invented by a German scientist, Paul Nipkow, in 1884. An image of the scene was formed on the rotating disc. Holes in the disc passed one at a time across the image, exposing a photoelectric cell behind the disc to each part of the image in return. Baird amplified the signals produced by the cell and used them to vary the brightness of a small neon lamp. A second scanning disc rotated in front of the lamp. As each hole in the disc passed quickly across the flickering lamp, it appeared to the eye to form a line of varying brightness. A complete image was built up in this way from a series of lines, scanned quickly, one after another.

Vladimir Zworykin (1889-1982), a Russian, contributed to the television system when he devised the iconoscope (electronic scanner) in the 1920's.

The iconoscope used the scanning principle to convert visual images into electrical signals, and Zworykin also developed the use of cathode ray tubes for displaying the images.

In 1939, Zworykin made modifications to the German made electron microscope making it possible for biologists to study viruses and protein molecules for the first time.

The first regular television broadcasts began in London in 1936.

The first system for commercial color television broadcasting was invented by the American, Peter C. Goldmark in 1940. The first regular television service began in the United States in 1954.

A color television camera contains tinted mirrors, called dichroic mirrors, which split up the light from the scene into blue, green, and red color components. The images are then scanned by three image-orthicon camera tubes, and three separate vision signals are produced.

W hen there seemed to be no more room for advancements, a discovery came to make smaller electronic circuits requiring less voltage and lasting longer.

It became a branch of science called *electronics*. It started with the vacuum tube. The disadvantage was the tube could not detect extremely short waves, those we call microwaves.

In 1874 a German physicist noticed that there existed a strange flow of current in certain materials. These were grouped under the name of *semiconductors*.

Semiconductors can conduct current better than an insulator, but not as good as a conductor.

Scientists began experimenting with silicon. The purest silicon was melted down and made into large bars. They found that there were two types of silicon: A positive and a negative type.

Another peculiarity of this crystal was that it acted as a rectifier. Early radios needed rectifiers because they could only operate on DC, so a special tube had been made that rectified AC to DC. Now there was something very small that could do the same thing without wasting a lot of voltage.

A number of experimenters did work in this area but nothing of significance was recognized until two days before Christmas in 1947, when three scientists, William Shockley, Walter Brattain, and John Bardeen, working at the Bell Telephone Laboratories, were working on a semiconductor germanium crystal. During their experimentation, they placed two tiny wires .002 inches apart. Upon making contact with the crystal's surface, to their surprise, a telephone voice was amplified 40 times. They discovered what is known as the "transistor effect" that provided a replacement for the vacuum tube. Because the transistor continues to shrink dramatically, miniaturization has reached a point where thousands of transistors and resistors are packed tightly together to form one integrated circuit.

Shockley, Brattain, and Bardeen received the 1956 Nobel prize in Physics for their amazing discovery.

There were still many problems as the early transistors were noisy and mechanically weak.

High quality transistors were produced replacing the vacuum tube. In 1954 a new way of refining geranium was discovered. That improved the transistor's behavior. 1955 was the beginning of the transistor age.Todays transistors are so small that a microscope is necessary to see them. Tens of thousands of transistors can fit into one microchip that is the size of an eraser on a pencil.

The difference between a vacuum tube and the transistor is that a tube works in a vacuum. A transistor works in solid material. That's why the term solid state is used when referring to transistorized equipment.

Transistors turn on instantly. They don't require a warm-up time like a tube does. They run cool and are very small and extremely rugged. A transistor will last for years and very little voltage is needed. A portable transistor radio will run for hundreds of hours on a 9-volt battery.

A transistor can take a tiny signal, so faint the sharpest ear cannot hear it, and amplifies the signal so it can fill a room with sound.

A transistor used as a switch operates at incredible speeds. Computers depend on switches. A computer operating at a few nanoseconds is considered slow. (A nanosecond is one billionth of a second).

Thousands of transistors can be packed together in one integrated chip that is no bigger than the smallest fingernail. When transistors are packed together in a tiny chip, it is called an *integrated* circuit. These circuits are found in televisions, computers, satellites, cameras, etc.

Today, a computer contains microprocessors made up of thousands of transistors and other devices, that years ago would have taken up a large room of equipment. Without computers there would be no space flights. And without the solar cells, we could not recharge the batteries used to power our space vehicles.

In 1832 Charles Babbage, a mathematics professor at Cambridge University England, invented the first general purpose computer.

The first automatic electronic digital computer was designed by an electrical engineer, J. Presper Eckert and physicist, John Mauchly in 1946. It weighed 30 tons, consuming 150 kw of power and used 1500 relays and 18,000 vacuum tubes and hundreds of thousands of other components.

Sir James Chadwick (1891-1974), a British physicist, is best known for his discovery of the *neutron*.

In 1911 Chadwick began research into the atomic structure which was to become a lifelong interest and which would eventually make him internationally famous.

Chadwick's discovery was a major breakthrough and the neutron soon proved to be a valuable tool in research and lead to the discovery of nuclear fission and the first nuclear reactor.

The use of neutrons in atomic fission led to the production of the atomic bomb. Chadwick was awarded the Nobel prize for physics in 1935 for his discovery.

Otto Hahn (1879-1968), a German chemist and physicist, made the vital discovery which led to the first nuclear reactor.

He uncovered the process of nuclear fission by which nuclei of atoms of heavy elements can break into smaller nuclei; in the process releasing large quantities of energy.

Hahn was awarded the Nobel prize for chemistry in 1944.

A device that separated electrons from protons by means of a moving belt called the *Van de Graaf generator* was devised by the American physicist Robert Van de Graaf in 1931. It was a big improvement over previous devices for developing energy for bombarding particles.

The machine he designed would collect and store huge amounts of electric charge. The charge builds up on a metal sphere and reaches an incredible 10 million volts. The machine is used mostly as a research tool for studying the particles that make up atoms.

The microwave oven is an ingenious appliance that uses microwaves to penetrate the food and heat it. Microwaves are nothing more than radio waves generated at a high frequency. These microwaves are generated by an electron tube called a *magnetron*.

A magnetron tube is capable of generating pulses of up to one billion hertz (one gigahertz). The tube was invented in 1940 by British researchers. The first domestic use was in the United States around 1947.

The use of microwaves for cooking was discovered in 1945 by an American, Percy Spencer. Microwave cooking is based on dielectric heating in which food is treated as a dielectric material or as a capacitor. The water molecules found in most foods vibrate under exposure to microwaves, resulting in rapid heating.

Alexandre Becquerel, a French physicist, experimented in 1857 with the electric discharge tube and found that suitable gases would fluoresce when their atoms were ionized by electrons. In 1910 Georges Claude produced a neon light. In 1939 fluorescent lighting, as it is known today, was demonstrated. It used mercury vapor to produce fluorescence in the phosphor coating on the inside of the tube.

Т
he idea of the heat pump is said to have originated
with scientist Lord Kelvin in 1852. It was not
until 1927 that a patent for a heat pump was
granted to the English inventor T.G.N. Haldane.

D.M. Chapin, C.S. Fuller, and G.L. Pearson at
Bell Laboratories in 1954 invented silicon batteries. A
means for converting sunlight directly to electricity. A
solar battery contains semiconductors which readily lose
electrons when exposed to sunlight. They have proved
useful in space vehicles as well as other devices.

The light produced by the laser is clearly no
ordinary kind of light. A remarkable piece of electrical
equipment used today by scientists, doctor's, as well as
the industry, is the *laser.*

The laser was invented by Theodore H. Maiman,
an American, in 1960. The name laser stands for "Light
Amplification by Stimulated Emission of Radiation".

The laser emits an almost perfect parallel beam.
Lasers find a variety of applications in measuring. Communications is another area that offers enormous potential
for lasers.

Listen to a compact disc audio recording and you
hear crystal-clear music read by a laser beam.

L asers today are doing many different jobs from communications to hospital and research laboratories to factories and construction sites.

Medical science had used lasers to repair the human eye and lasers have been used to produce holes in very hard material such as diamonds.

It has been written that the ancient Egyptians recognized and used the therapeutic power of light as long as 6,000 years ago on patches of depigmented skin that were cosmetically undesirable. Egyptian healers would crush a plant similar to parsley and rub the affected areas with the leaves. Exposure to the sun's radiation produced a severe form of sunburn only in the treated areas.

Radio waves and visible light are both a form of electromagnetic radiation. The only difference is in their wavelengths. The single wavelength quality of the radiation from a laser is similar to that of a radio transmitter. Information that can be carried by electromagnetic waves is proportional to the frequency. More information can be carried as the frequency is increased. The laser beam is so much higher in frequency than radio frequencies that it might be possible for one laser beam to carry several million radio transmissions.

The laser can perform its many miracles because it produces a beam of coherent light. In this kind of light, all the waves vibrate exactly together. All the waves reinforce each other, producing light of great energy.

Fiber optics were invented in 1955 by an Indian physicist Narinder S. Kapany. By means of total reflection, thin glass fibers can transmit light with little loss of intensity. The invention of the laser in 1960 and of production techniques for glass fibers in 1970 greatly speeded up the development of fiber optics.

Fiber optics (piping light) is the science that deals with the transmission of light through extremely thin fibers of glass, plastic, or other transparent material. The fibers are provided as a single fiber or a cable bundle. They may be bent or curved (within limits) to meet the needs of special routing.

Fiber optics now has a permanent position in the electronic revolution. It is used instead of electrical wire because the fibers are extremely small, light in weight, and virtually immune to electrical interference. They will neither radiate outward the signal they carry, nor are they susceptible to the acceptance of induced signals.

Today telephone companies rely heavily on fiber optic cable for higher transmission speed and for longer distances. The cable is made with no electrical conductors, so they won't carry dangerous current pulses injected by lightning strikes.

Trains that will seem to run faster than a speeding bullet, magnets more powerful than a locomotive, home computers able to do your income taxes at a single bound. It's superconductor!

The science of very low temperatures is known as cryogenics. Helium remains liquid even near absolute zero unless it is compressed, but loses all viscosity and becomes a superfluid. It will flow up the walls of a container and over the top.

When metals are cooled to temperatures near absolute zero, most of them become excellent conductors of electricity, with electrons flowing without significant resistance. *Superconductivity* was discovered by Kamerlingh Onnes of Holland in 1911.

Heike Kamerlingh Onnes received the Nobel prize for his discovery.

An important discovery made in 1986 by J. Georg Bednorz of Germany and K. Alex Muller of Switzerland showed that certain materials became superconductors at higher temperatures than any previously known. The two men won the Nobel prize in 1987.

ENERGY

The tendency of matter to resist change is called inertia (in nur sha). The word inert means sluggish to change and lackadaisical. The animating force that prevents inertia from taking over is called *energy*.

What does energy mean? In one sense it means power.

The word energy is derived from two Greek words; en meaning in and ergon meaning work. Energy means *in work* or the ability to do work.

Actually there are two forms of energy; *heat* and *motion*. Heat and motion in all their various forms can be converted into each other.

Heat from a gas flame causes water to steam. This is an example of heat converted to motion. You can also convert motion to heat by rubbing two sticks together. Fire is a *form* of heat as water is a *form* of motion. So heat and motion are forms of energy, *not* energy itself.

The Law of Conservation of Energy states that *energy is neither created nor destroyed.* The total amount of energy in the universe always remains the same.

Mechanical energy can be converted to electrical energy or electrical energy can be converted to mechanical energy. No matter how *energy* is changed, or what form it takes, the total amount of energy in the universe always remains the same.

Energy is motion (kinetic) or it can be stored (potential). Anything held in your hand has potential energy. When the item is dropped from your hand it creates energy with motion as it falls.

A ball held in your hand has potential energy and when thrown through the air the energy is converted to kinetic energy, as well as heat. The motion of the moving ball makes the air molecules around it start moving. The air becomes hotter and the ball itself becomes warmer. With all these forms of converted energy - the mechanical energy of moving air molecules and the total heat gain of the ball and the air around it - when added together will equal the original amount of potential energy when the ball was held in your hand.

The six major forms of energy are chemical, mechanical, electrical, light, heat, and nuclear.

Chemical energy is food and fuels. Energy can be converted into any other form of energy.

For a long time humans had been running around the earth with human muscle power as the only source of energy. Then the discovery of fire helped us warm ourselves, but the harnessing of mechanical energy led to the greatest expansion in human productive power.

The most significant change came, however, with the development of steam engines and the discovery of electricity. Now almost every corner of the world can be populated.

E lectricity is one of the most important forms of energy and it cannot even be seen, heard, or smelt. The quiet giant!

Sources of energy we use are:

PETROLEUM (oil) provides almost half of the energy used in the world.

COAL developed from the remains of plants that died 400 million years ago. It provides about 30% of the world's energy.

NATURAL GAS provides about 20% of the world's energy.

Others are *WATER POWER* which costs nothing, causes no pollution, and cannot be used up. However, expensive dams or other structures are needed as the water must fall from a higher place to a lower place.

WOOD, that was once the main fuel, is still a large source of energy.

NUCLEAR ENERGY from fission is also used to generate electricity. A huge amount of energy can be obtained from a small amount of fuel.

SOLAR ENERGY is used in small applications. It is clean and unlimited, but it needs a large area of land for the collectors and is interrupted by darkness and bad weather.

Coal is abundant enough to last 300 or 400 more years. It now provides about a third of the world's energy and about a fifth of the energy used in the United States.

The amount of fossil fuels (oil, natural gas, and coal) consumed in the United States has nearly doubled every 20 years since 1900. Between 1960 and 1980, the U.S. population increased by 25%. Total energy demand, however, rose by 80%. More than three times as much as the population.

As Nations shift from agricultural to industrial economies, vast increases in energy consumption occur for powering industry and for mechanizing and fertilizing farms.

A major trend in energy demand has been a dramatic increase in the use of electricity. In 1980 the U.S. used 380 times more electricity than it did in 1900.

Experts forecast that fossil fuels will still meet more than 75% of the world energy needs by the year 2000. By the year 2000, hydropower is expected to decline and nuclear power to increase to about 11% of the U.S. needs.

Environmental problems, particularly air polution, will restrict the use of coal. Coal-burning plants release sulphur dioxide, which combines with moisture in the air to produce acid rain. This destroys forests and lakes, and damages buildings.

Natural gas, which supplies about 25% of the U.S. energy needs, is on the decline since consumption has exceeded the discovery of new sources. Experts predict that natural gas will satisfy only about 10% of the U.S. energy needs by the year 2000. The decline of reserves is a concern since natural gas is the cleanest fossil fuel.

Although hydropower is historically an important energy source, its growth potential is limited because few suitable sites exist for new hydroelectric plants.

Experts say the world's oil supply began declining around 1990, and by the year 2050 we will have used up the two trillion barrels of crude oil accumulated since prehistoric times. The conclusion is obvious and urgent! We must develop other available energy sources fast.

Solar power is still distant as the sun is too difficult to harness. It would take 8000 square miles of collectors. Example: A 7 foot diameter collector = 100 watts.

A greater growth is seen in the future for nuclear energy. Nuclear reactions are created by uranium. It is not burned like coal or oil, but produces extreme heat as the atoms are split. It's like a large furnace but no fuel is burning.

Coal costs several hundred million dollars more than nuclear power. Unlike coal there is an abundant supply of uranium. Coal fired is a thermal plant which is called a *swing* plant. As the peak times occur a thermal plant can swing into production in a matter of a few hours, where as a nuclear plant generally takes *2 days*.

The atoms of most elements, such as iron, are stable and unchanging over time, but the atoms of some elements - radium, uranium, and others - do change. These unstable atoms are *radioactive*.

With nuclear energy the activity occurs in the nucleus of the atoms. These are called nuclear reactions, and matter *can be gained or destroyed*. The splitting of the atom is the twisting of the arm of mother nature.

Albert Einstein (1879-1955). Einstein's formula proved that one gram of mass can be converted into a torrential amount of energy. To do this, the activity of the atoms has to occur in the nucleus.

E = energy, M = mass, and C = the speed of light which is 186,000 miles per second. When you square 186,000 you can see it would only take a small amount of mass to produce a huge amount of energy.

93

Always remember, the total amount of energy in the universe always remains the same.

We don't create electricity, we *produce* electricity. When a building burns it is not destroyed. The basic matter of which the building was constructed has been converted into ashes, and part into heat that dissipated into the air. But the matter is still there somewhere. Even if we can't see it, touch it, or smell it.

Mechanical energy can be converted to electrical energy or electrical energy can be converted to mechanical energy. No matter how *energy* is changed, or what form it takes, the total amount of energy in the universe always remains the same.

We will consume more energy in the next 5 years than was consumed by all previous society in the history of the world.

Man must find new ways to create electrical energy as the fossil fuel supply dwindles. It is estimated that by the year 2020 nuclear energy will generate the huge amounts that we depend on today; the six trillion watts each day.

If you have trouble relating to six trillion watts, a human being operates on 100 watts. The brain 20 watts and the body 80 watts. You are equivalent to a 100 watt light bulb.

NUCLEAR ENERGY

In the year 1930 scientists used parts of atoms such as protons, neutrons, or electrons and hurled them at nucleus at tremendous speeds so they would get inside the nucleus. With these atom smashers they discovered by splitting the atom of uranium 235 they had a process called *fission* (fish-in).

The neutron splits a nucleus in two. As it splits, the nucleus throws off extra neutons. This chain reaction continues as billions of fission reactions happen in a second. Vast amounts of energy are given off when the nucleus changes.

Isotope is an atom that has the same number of protons but a different number of neutrons than the usual atoms of an element. Although the charge remains the same, its weight varies depending on the number of neutrons in its nucleus.

Uranium 235; the 235 refers to the isotopes weight, which is the total sum of its protons and neutrons.

In the nuclear power plant the uranium 235 pellets produce extreme heat in their tubes thus heating the water jackets to produce steam to turn the turbine generators. The danger of fission is the radioactive material called radiation.

A much safer nuclear energy is called *fusion* (fuse-in). Fusion is the joining of hydrogen atoms which causes heat hotter than the sun. Extreme heat is needed to start a fusion reaction. Most likely, lasers will be used for this source of heat. Fusion reactors are not in use yet and are still being experimented with as we have no materials to contain this extreme heat. Fusion emits no radioactive waste and is fueled by the safe and abundant hydrogen. The hydrogen atom is the lightest atom and the most susceptible to fusion. Hydrogen is the most abundant of all atoms. It can be found in every ocean.

Fission and fusion are the two basic kinds of nuclear reactions. Fission and fusion *never* start naturally.

It took over 40 years to learn how to tame the nucleus of the atom and manipulate it to create nuclear energy.

The first atomic bomb, in 1945, was a chain reaction that raced uncontrollably. Today in nuclear power plants it can be controlled, slowed down, and completely stopped. We have come a long way since 1945.

A nuclear reactor produces heat by splitting uranium atoms. The heat boils water into high-pressure steam that drives an electrical generator.

The nuclear reactor uses *heavy water* to transfer heat and to help control the nuclear reaction.

Heavy water is a clear, colorless liquid that looks and tastes like ordinary tap water. It occurs naturally in water in minute quantities; about one part heavy water to 7,000 parts of ordinary water.

Unlike normal water, which is composed of hydrogen and oxygen, heavy water is made up of deuterium and oxygen. The name heavy water stems from the presence of deuterium, which is a form of hydrogen that has an extra neutron in its atomic nucleus and weighs slightly more than ordinary hydrogen. As a result, heavy water is about 10% heavier than normal water. It also has different freezing and boiling points.

Heavy water is about 30 times better than ordinary water in slowing down the neutrons without absorbing them.

Roughly 340,000 tons of lake water are needed to produce one ton of heavy water.

A nuclear reactor can NOT explode like a bomb. A bomb has a much higher percentage of uranium for fission.

The disadvantage is after used fuel has been removed from a reactor by remotely controlled equipment, it is stored in water-filled pools, called fuel bats, located on site at the generating station. The water cools the fuel and serves as a radiation shield.

After six years in water storage, used fuel gives off much less heat than when it first entered the fuel bay. At this time, it can either remain in water or be transferred to large, above ground, dry storage containers made of steel and concrete.

These containers provide physical containment for the waste and shielding against radiation, but they have a number of advantages, including the fact that they require less maintenance than water filled storage bays. In addition, they provide secure long term storage, should there be a delay in developing a permanent disposal site for unused nuclear fuel.

Most of the energy on earth comes from the sun. It is solar energy, produced by atomic reactions inside the sun that creates the energy stored beneath the surface of our planet. The type of atomic reaction that occurs inside the sun is called nuclear *fusion*.

A scientist, Robert Golka, used Nikola Tesla's notes to build a repilica of his high-voltage machine. He sees the machine as the means to achieve nuclear fusion. Fusion creates a sharp burst of intense heat by striking two atoms together. This form of nuclear energy would give the world a source of power without contaminating the air, the land, and the water as it would produce no radioactive substances.

In fusion, the atom implodes (crushes). This crushing of the atom creates a chain reaction in which millions of other atoms are crushed. The matter result is the release of tremendous amounts of heat and light energy.

Another type of atomic energy is *fission*, the splitting of the atom, it splits other atoms, causing a chain reaction that releases heat and light. *Uranium* atoms are used in nuclear power plants. The heat energy from fission is used to make steam to turn the turbine generator.

Scientists today are working on a fusion generator. Fusion is much safer because it does not give off any deadly radiation. *Deuterium* is used for fuel and its supply is virtually inexhaustible.

Nuclear power is now supplementing the traditional prime movers; coal, oil, natural gas, and hydro- power. This new expensive source of power will furnish most of our power in the future.

SOLAR ENERGY

The idea of being able to get useful energy from the sun has been a dream of scientists for centuries. The sun is an inexhaustible source of energy, and sunlight is available all over the earth. What is needed to utilize the energy in sunlight is some efficient way to convert the radiant energy in sunlight into some form of energy that is easier to use, such as electrical energy. The silicone voltaic cell, or solar cell as it is commonly called, is just such a device.

The photovoltaic effect, where electricity is produced when certain materials are illuminated, is not new. It was first discovered in 1839 by E. Becqueral. Thus, the photovoltaic cell is probably the first solid-state electronic device ever invented.

The first significant use of the photovoltaic cells to produce electricity was in the space program. Satellites need a source of electrical energy that will last for a long time without any attention. All conventional batteries will run down after a period of time. The solar cell, however, will continue to deliver electrical power as long as sunlight is available.

The sun has four million tons of mass that are converted into energy every second that produce 380, 000, 000, 000, 000, 000, 000, 000, 000 watts of energy.

Electricity has one disadvantage. It cannot be stored on a large scale. Late at night very little electricity is used as most people are asleep. Peak times are in the winter, in early morning, and in the evening when people get home from work.

A supply of electricity must always meet the demand. This is achieved by shutting down and starting up power station generators as requirements vary.

Each power station has a control room where staff monitor the moment-to-moment variations in demand, and supervise the amount of electricity generated.

The development of the power grid, whereby many power plants are interconnected and feed power collectively to points of greatest demand according to changing conditions is used throughout the United States.

Hoover Dam, on the Colorado river, has water passing through 17 turbine generator's producing 4 billion kilowatts of energy a year: Enough for 500,000 homes.

It takes these 15 million men and women in the electrical industry working 24 hours a day, everyday, to keep the lights burning.

The world lives and works at the end of a wire.

101

Index

A

B

Brattain, Walter 79
Brown, A.K. 58, 59

C

Canada 3
Capacitor 9
Carbon lamp 45
Carbon rods 43
Cardan, Jerome 4
Carrier wave 74
Cathode 30
Cathode ray 72
Cathode tube 75, 77
Chadwick, Sir James 81
Chapin, D.M. 84
Chicago Worlds Fair 52
Claude, Georges 83
Coal 65, 89 - 92, 98
Code 65
Color television 77
Columbian Exposition 52, 60
Columbus, Christopher 3
Commutator 31
Compass needle 23
Computer 80, 81
Computers 74
Condensed 9
Conduction 6
Conductors 6
Constitution 11

Continental Edison Company 49
Copper 14
Copper disk 15
Copper sulfate 18
Coulomb 17
Crookes, William 72
Crystal 40
Curie point 40
Curie, Pierre 40

D

Daniell, John F. 18
Darcey, Henry 38
Davy, Sir Humphry 16, 29, 43
De Coulomb, Charles A. 17
De Magnete 5
DeForest, Lee 74
Degausser 36
Deuterium 98
Diathermy 50
Diode 73
Direct current 15, 50
Directly proportional 25
Discharges 15
Dishwasher 52
Dry cell 18
Dufay 8
Dynamo 17, 30, 41, 42, 63

E

Eckert, J. Presper 81
Edison Machine Works 50
Edison Plant 61
Edison, Thomas Alva 43 - 46, 49, 50, 57 - 58, 60, 62, 63
Efficient motors 33
Einstein, Albert 39, 92
Einthoven, William 70
Electric clock 52
Electric Code 65
Electric fluid 8, 11
Electric generator 30
Electric locomotion 28
Electric meter 63
Electrical impulses 38
Electrical radiation waves 70
Electrics 4
Electrocuted 11
Electrolysis 16, 17, 30
Electrolyte 30
Electromagnet 24
Electromagnetic induction 29, 32
Electromagnetic waves 69
Electromagnetism 22, 32
Electron 72
Electronic communication 34
Electronic scanner 76
Electronics 78
Electroplating 42

Elektron 2
Energy 88

F

Farad 31
Faraday cage 6
Faraday, Michael 15, 29 - 33
Fessenden, R.A. 74
Fiber optics 86
Fine-wire magnet 33
Fire Underwriters 65
First electric motor 24
First electrician 11
Fission 96, 98
Fission reactions 94
Fleming valve 73
Fleming, John A. 73
Fluorescent lighting 83
FM frequency 74
Fossil fuels 90
Franklin, Benjamin 9 - 12
Frequencies 69
Fritts, Charles 75
Frog 14
Fuller, C.S. 84
Fusion 95, 97, 98

G

Galvani, Luigi 14, 16
Galvanic electricity 14

Galvanometer 22
Gauss 36, 37
Gauss, Karl Friedrich 36
General Electric 60, 62, 63
Generating plant 45
Generator 41
Geneve 34
Geranium 79
Gigahertz 83
Gilbert, William 4 - 6, 8
Girard, Pierre-Simon 64
Goat Island 55
Goldmark, Peter C. 77
Governor 13
Gramme, Zenobe 42
Gravitation 7
Gray, Stephen 6, 7, 34
Greeks 1

H

Hahn, Otto 82
Haldane, T.G.N. 84
Hand-cranked generator 31
Harmonics 68
Heat 19, 20
Heat pump 84
Heavy water 95, 96
Helmholtz, Hermann von 68
Henry 33
Henry, Joseph 32 - 35

Hertz 70, 74
Hertz, Heinrich 69 - 71, 75
Heterodyne 74
Hoover Dam 100
Hydroelectric generators 61
Hydroelectric plants 49, 50
Hydrogen 15, 95
Hydropower 90, 98
Hysteresis 63

I

Iconoscope 76, 77
Incandescent lamp 43, 45
Incandescent light 44
Induces 32
Induction 33
Insulator 9
Insulators 6
Integrated circuit 80
Invisible force 22
Invisible glue 4
Ion 30
Isotope 94

J

Japan 3
Joule, James Prescott 19, 20

K

Kapany, Narinder S. 86
Kelvin scale 21
Key 11
Kinetic theory 21
King 43
Kirchhoff, Gustav R. 38
Kite 10, 11
Kite experiment 9

L

Laser 84, 85, 86, 95
Laws of Motion 7
Leclanche, Georges 18
Lenard, Philipp 75
Lenz's law 27
Lenz, Heinrich E. 27
Lesage 34
Leyden jar 9, 28
Lightning 9 - 11
Lightning rod 10
Like charges 8
Lodestone 1 - 4
Lord Kelvin 20, 60, 84
Lord Rayleigh 68
Lorentz, Hendrik A. 75

M

Mach, Ernst 68

Magnesia 2
Magnet 33
Magnetic effect 22
Magnetic field 21
Magnetism 21, 22
Magnetron 83
Maiman, Theodore H. 84
Marconi, Guglielmo 53, 70, 71, 73
Mauchly, John 81
Maxwell 39
Maxwell, James Clerk 21, 39
Medical diathery 52
Microchip 79
Microprocessors 80
Microwave 52
Microwave oven 83
Microwaves 78, 83
Morgan, J.P. 52
Morse, Samuel 34, 35
Motor 41
Muller, K. Alex 87

N

Nanosecond 80
Natural gas 89, 91, 98
Negative charge 9,10
Neutron 81
Newton, Isaac 7, 39
Niagara Falls 50, 55, 56, 60, 61
Nipkow, Paul 76

Nobel prize 71, 75, 79, 81, 82, 87
Nobili, Leopold 22
Nollet 8
North pole 3
Nuclear energy 90, 94
Nuclear fission 81, 82
Nuclear power 90
Nuclear reactor 81, 82

O

Oersted, Hans Christian 21, 23, 29
Ohm 26
Ohm, Georg Simon 25
Onnes, Heike Kamerlingh 87

P

Pacinotti, Antoni 41
Parsons, Sir Charles Algernon 64
Pearl Street 61
Pearson, G.L. 84
Peltier effect 26, 27
Peltier, Jean Charles 26
Permeability 38
Permeate 38
Petroleum 89
Philadelphia 10
Phonograph 44
Photoelectric cell 75, 76
Photoelectric effect 75
Photographic mind 48

Photovoltaic cell 99
Photovoltaic effect 99
Piezein 40
Piezoelectric effect 40
Piezoelectricity 40
Pigeons 3, 53, 54
Pixii's machine 31
Pixii, Hippolyte 31
Plante, Gaston 18
Platinum element 45
Positive charge 9,10
Potassium 16
Power grid 100
Powerhouse 46
Priestley, Joseph 12

R

Radar 74
Radiant energy 39
Radiation 97
Radio 36, 69, 73, 74
Radio transmitters 70
Radio waves 52
Radioactivity 21
Radioactve 92
Radiothermy 50
Rectifier 73
Rectifiers 78
Relay 33
Relays 81

Resin rod 8
Resinous 8,10
Richmann 11
Right-hand grip 23
Robotics 52
Roosevelt, Eleanor 54

S

Salt acid solution 15
Sand-filled pipe 38
Satellites 80, 99
Seebeck effect 26
Seebeck, Thomas 26
Self charging 15
Self-induction 33
Semiconductors 78
Shock 8
Shockley, William 79
Siemens, Sir William 28
Siemens, Werner von 42
Silicon 78
Silicon batteries 84
Sodium 16
Solar cell 99
Solar cells 80
Solar energy 90, 91, 97, 99
Solid state 80
Sound 37, 66 - 68
South pole 3
Spark transmitter 70

Spectroscope 38
Spectroscopy 38
Speed of light 38
Spencer, Percy 83
Sprengel, Hermann 43
Stanley, William 56
Starr 43
Static electricity 5, 28
Steam 64
Steam engine 13
Steam turbine 64
Steel refinement 28
Steinmetz, Charles 63
Sturgeon, William 24, 32
Sulfuric acid 18
Sulphur 5
Superconductivity 87
Superconductor 87
Superheterodyne 74
Swan, Sir Joseph 43
Swimmers rule 23

T

Telegraph 34, 35, 44, 69
Telegraphy 36
Telephone 44, 67 - 69, 86
Television 36, 69, 72, 74 - 77
Tesla coil 51
Tesla, Nikola 47 - 55, 57 - 62
Thales of Miletus 1

Watt

Ampere

Volta

Ohm